"G I JOE"

"G I JOE"

("PRIVATE BREGER")

FROM THE PAGES OF

YANK AND STARS AND STRIPES

BY LT. DAVE BREGER

BLUE RIBBON BOOKS

GARDEN CITY, N. Y.

IN MEMORY OF
SGT. PETE PARIS
ON
JUNE 6, 1944

FOREWORD

LAST July 25, 1944 in the hedgerows near Pont Hebert on the St. Lo sector I went up to a forward position, passing tanks, wire details, ambulances and soldiers going up and coming back and all the other life that you see on a road on the way to the front lines. Finally I came to a stretch that was very quiet and I was frightened because it was my first time up to the front. A bit farther up I came upon men resting in a ditch behind a hedgerow. I asked them where the front was and one G I said, this is it. They told me that they were resting in this place because they had dropped back from their front line positions as we were going to stage the greatest air bombing show in history. I noticed that most of them were reading *Stars and Stripes* and wanting very much to make conversation that wasn't about death and wounds and horror, I mentioned that I was a friend of Lt. Breger at whose "Private Breger" cartoon they had just been looking. They surrounded me and excitedly asked me dozens of questions about Breger. What does he look like? Does he look like "Private Breger?" Does he think of his own ideas? Does he do them all by hand? And they told me that they wished I were Lt. Breger, so I could sign their short snorters and maybe make a drawing of "Private Breger."

With this successful breaking of the ice I was able to get really close to them and make my own drawings and get my story.

As a friend of Lt. ("Private") Breger I was able to get close to a great number of G I's from St. Lo all the way into Germany. A soldier at the front this winter doesn't have much in the way of fun. There are no girls but German girls, and it's an $85 fine if you fraternize. If you buy an ice cream cone in Belgium it costs you a $10 fine because you are upsetting civilian economy. You eat the same food you have been eating for five or six months or a year past.

Sometimes it's K rations. If you are way up close there is stuff coming over all the time, so there are not often USO shows or donut mobiles or Bing Crosby or Bob Hope. It is not safe to kick a football around, so just about the only fun you have are the cartoons in *Stars and Stripes* which somehow manages every morning to be delivered to your foxhole doorstep. Recently in the Huertgen Forest in Germany a wet and muddy G I sat back from his labor digging his sixth foxhole that day and told me that the only time he had laughed in a week was over the "Private Breger" cartoon in that day's rain-soaked copy of *Stars and Stripes*.

So there are millions of American guys who have been to war and who will never forget "Private Breger."

It took this war to give Breger the vehicle he needed to become the cartoonist he is. His cartoons were always good. They always had the universal elements which are true of a good postage stamp or of a mural in the Sistine Chapel, that is, drawing, design and composition, plus the extra undefinable something that all the good things have.

When he went into the Army, he didn't go in as a celebrity. He went in as a G I, a private, and was among the first to be drafted. He thought his cartoonist career was over when he was sent to Motor Maintenance at Camp Livingston, Louisiana. He could have taken it "easy," if anyone can possibly take it easy as a G I, and not stayed up drawing his cartoons in the camp bakery shop which was the only place where the lights were on all night; nor did he have to draw his cartoons by the light in the cab of an ordnance truck when he was on maneuvers, but he did. Out of all this work came "Private Breger" and "G I Joe." Of course, now Breger's a celebrity, a lieutenant (at this writing) and famous wherever American soldiers are.

The end of the war, which he is hastening with his helping of soldier morale, will certainly not be the end of Breger. No doubt "Private Breger" will be returned to civilian life, and if it isn't "Civilian Breger" it will be "Civilian Jones" or "Civilian Brown" or some other little guy with freckles and wearing glasses whom Breger will create to keep up civilian morale, if civilian morale will need any keeping up in those happiest of happy days in the postwar world.

JOHN GROTH

THE BIRTH OF "G I JOE"

"G I Joe" and "Private Breger" were identical twins, although the latter was born almost a year earlier

In the spring of 1942, a year after I had been inducted into the Army (and assigned to repairing trucks in Louisiana), I was transferred to the newly organized staff of *Yank, The Army Weekly*. By that time I had reached the grade of corporal.

"Look here," the *Yank* authorities said to me, "We want you to do a cartoon feature like your 'Private Breger' in *The Saturday Evening Post*—but give him a different name."

And so, like an amoeba, "Private Breger" split in two, and I called his twin "G I Joe." Thus it was that in the first issue of *Yank*, June 17, 1942. "G I Joe" was born. His full name was "G I Joe" Trooper.

"G I Joe," "Private Breger" and I (Staff Sergeant Technician Breger) were all shipped to England in the early summer of 1942, together with a fellow-sergeant of *Yank*. We were the very first correspondents to be sent overseas by *Yank*.

Eventually, while in England, I was commissioned a second lieutenant and this collided head-on with the basic policy of *Yank:* "By Enlisted Men Only." However, *Stars and Stripes*, the Army daily in the European Theater of Operations, had no similar policy. So "G I Joe," "Private Breger" and I (Second Lieutenant Breger) were transferred to *Stars and Stripes*. And there "G I Joe" continued appearing until the spring of 1944.

Incidentally, I would like to express my appreciation for the patience and toleration of Captain William W. Wilcox of Omaha, Nebraska. For it was during our countless lunches in England that I regularly inflicted him with contemplated "G I Joe" gags for my next cartoon. Last I heard of Bill was that he is somewhere in France.

But, like much else in this war, duplication of efforts had to be eliminated. So "Private Breger" carried on alone and "G I Joe" was liquidated. In his place I have created another cartoon character: "G I Jerry," an unpleasant German soldier (or is that redundant?), by which satire and ridicule on Nazi philosophy are appropriately expressed. Like "G I Joe" used to, "G I Jerry" currently appears in the European editions of *Stars and Stripes*.

While my original portrayal of "G I Joe" now carries on through his twin brother "Private Breger," his name has become representative of the American soldier everywhere. Therefore, I would like to advance a modest claim to fame as the creator, as far as I know, of "G I Joe," born in *Yank*, June 17, 1942.

LT. DAVE BREGER

Classification

Dave Breger
Britain

Articles of War
Part I

Dave Breger
Britain

I DON'T GIVE A DAMN *WHERE* YOU BEEN OR *WHO* YOUR FRIEND IS! YOU'RE GONNA GET IT FOR MISSING ROLL CALL LAST 3 DAYS!

ART. 61 - Any person subject to military law who... absents himself from his command...

I HOPE YOU REALIZE THE SERIOUSNESS OF WHAT YOU'RE DOING!

ART. 58 - Any person subject to military law who deserts ... the service of the U.S....

ART. 54–Any person who shall procure himself to be enlisted in the military service of the U.S. by means of wilful misrepresentation or concealment...

ART. 41– Cruel and unusual punishment ...including flogging, branding, marking or tattooing, on the body, are prohibited

ART.59– Any person subject to military law who... persuades... another to desert the service of the U.S. ...

Articles of War
Part II

Lt. Dave Breger
Britain

ART. 66 — Any person subject to military law who... excites... any mutiny or sedition...

ART. 64 — Any person subject to military law who, on any pretense whatsoever, strikes his superior officer.

ART. 62 – Any [soldier] who uses disrespectful words against the President Vice President... Congress of the U.S....

ART. 63 – Any person subject to milita[ry] law who behaves with disrespect towa[rd] his superior officer...

ART. 65 – Any soldier who... uses insulting language... toward noncommissioned officer...

Articles of War Part III

Dave Breger
Britain

ART. 67 — Any... soldier who, being present at any mutiny.... does not use his utmost endeavor to suppress the same...

ART. 68 — All... noncommissioned officers have power to... quell all quarrels... and to order officers who take part in the same into confinement

ART. 70 - When any person subject to military law is placed in arrest... immediate steps will be taken to try the person accused...

RT. 69 - Any person subject to litary law charged with crime shall be placed in confinement

ART. 73 - Any person... wh without proper authorit releases any prisoner..

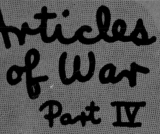

Articles of War
Part IV

Lt. Dave Breger
Britain

YOU KNOW THE PENALTY FOR BUSTING INTO SOMETHING LOCKED!

ART. 78 - Any person... who in time of war, forces a safeguard...

CAN'T BE HELPED, SIR! IT'S OUR COUNTERSIGN FOR TONIGHT!

ART. 77 - Any person... who... gives a... countersign different from that which he received...

ART. 75 - Any . . . . soldier who, before the enemy, runs away . . .

ART. 76 - Any person . . . who . . . attempt to compel any commander of any . . post . . . to abandon it . . .

ART. 79 - All . . . property taken from the enemy . . . shall be secured for the service of the United States . . .

Articles of War Part V

Dave Breger
Captain

ART. 84 — Any soldier who... disposes of... any horse... issued for use in the military service...

T. 82 — Any person who in e of war shall be found king.. about any...quarters...

RT. 83 - Any person . . . who wilfully suffers to be lost . . . any military property belonging to the U.S. . . .

ART. 81 - Whosoever relieves or attempts relieve the enemy with arms, ammunition, supplies . . .

RT. 80 - Any person subject to military law who . . . fails . . . to turn over captured property . . . without delay . . .

Articles of War

Part VI

t. Dave Breger
Britain

ART. 88 - Any person subject to military law who... interferes with any person bringing provisions... to the camp...

RT. 87 - Any [commanding] officer... who, or his private advantage.... is interested in he sales of any victuals brought into... camp

ART. 86- Any sentinel who is found...
sleeping upon his post...

ART. 89-... Any person subject to military
law who... destroys any property whats-
ever (unless by order of his C.O.)...

ART. 85- Any person subject to military law... who is found drunk on duty

Articles of War
Part VII

Lt. Dave Breger
Britain

ART. 94 — Any person... who... forges.. any signature upon any writing...

ART. 92 — Any person subject to military law who commits murder...

ART. 91- Any person subject to military law who fights or promotes or is concerned in or connives at fighting a duel...

ART. 90- No person subject to military law shall use any reproachful...speeches... to another

ART. 93- Any person... who commits manslaughter, mayhem, arson, burglary, housebreaking, robbery, larceny, embezzlement, perjury, forgery, sodomy, assault...

Articles
of War
Part VIII

Dave Breger
Britain

ART. 95 – Any officer... who is convicted of conduct unbecoming an officer and a gentleman...

I'M AFRAID IT'S NO USE, CAPTAIN!

PLEASE, PLEASE! DON'T HAVE ME ORDER AN INQUIRY *NOW*! WE'LL NEVER CRITICIZE YOUR MARKSMANSHIP AGAIN!

ART. 97 – ...A court of inquiry shall not be ordered by any C.O. except upon the request of the soldier whose conduct is to be inquired into

ART. 96 - ... All conduct of a nature to the prejudice of good order and military discipline... of which persons... are guilty...

ART. 99 - The party whose conduct is being inquired into shall have the right to be represented... by counsel of his own selection

ART. 98 - A court of inquiry shall consist of three or more officers...

Articles of War
of War
Part IX

Lt Dave Breger
Britain

...AND THIS UNFORTUNATE
SOLDIER, WITH THE
BEST INTENTIONS...
ETC., ETC

ART. 103- Each court of inquiry shall keep a record of its proceedings...

ADJUTANT'S OFFICE SPEAKING.
A REQUEST HEREWITH NOTED
FROM CONVENING COURT OF
INQUIRY FOR PERMISSION TO
EXPRESS OPINION THAT THE
ATTITUDE OF SOLDIER KNOWN AS
G.I. JOE, PRIVATE, 32091293, STINKS ON ICE. PURSUANT
TO AUTHORITY VESTED IN THE CONGRESS OF THE
UNITED STATES SAID REQUEST MUST BE SUBMITTED IN
TRIPLICATE TOGETHER WITH EIGHT LETTERS OF
RECOMMENDATION, ENDORSED BY CHIEF OF RED
TAPE SECTION, E.T.O., S.O.S., S.O.B., SUBJECT TO
REVIEW BY ANTI-PERSONNEL OFFICER, WITH
CONFIRMING CABLE FROM CHUNGKING...

ART. 102- A court... shall not give an opinion... unless specially ordered to do so...

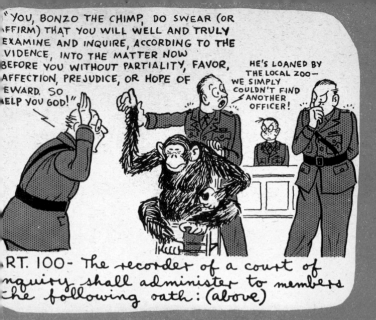

ART. 100— The recorder of a court of inquiry shall administer to members the following oath: (above)

ART. 104 — Any person punished...who deems his punishment unjust...may, through the proper channel, appeal to the next...authority, but may in meantime...undergo the punishment adjudged

ART. 101— The party whose conduct is being inquired into or his counsel...shall be permitted to examine...witnesses...

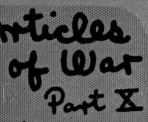

Articles of War
Part X

t. Dave Breger
Britain

YOUR DISCHARGE ON ACCOUNT OF BAD EYES JUST CAME THROUGH!

ART. 108- No enlisted man ... shall be discharged from ... service without a certificate of discharge ...

DDY CASE! WHEN ALL E YANKS WENT HOME BACK IN 1945 THEY KED US TO HOLD HIS ONE PENDING HIS ELEASE IN ANOTHER WO YEARS, SEVEN MONTHS, 3 DAYS...

T. 107- Every soldier who... deserts... or ...absents nself... or ...confined... or through ...drugs... liquor isease... or injury, rendering himself unable to per- m duty, shall [make good the time lost]...

"I, GIUSEPPE D'ALESSIO, DO SOLEMNLY SWEAR A (OR AFFIRMA) DAT I WILL BEAR A TRUE FAIT' AN' ALLEGIANCE TO DE UNITA STATES OF AMER'CA; DAT I WILL SERVA DEM HONESTLY AN' FAIT'FULLY AGAINST ALLA DER ENEMIES WHATSOEVER; AN' DAT I WILLA OBEY DE ORDERS OFA DE PRESIDENT OFA DE U.S. AN' DE ORDERS OFA DE OFFICERS APPOINTED OVER A ME, ACCORDIN' TO DE RULES AN' ARTICLES OFA WAR."

'S TOO IMPATIENT WAIT FOR ONE OUR OWN FICERS!

ART. 109 - At the time of his enlistment every oldier shall take the following oath (above): is oath... may be taken before any officer.

DRIVING THROUGH A RED LIGHT, IS IT? COME ALONG WITH ME!

PAY NO ATTENTION TO HIM! AS YOUR COMMANDING OFFICER I ORDER YOU TO DRIVE ON!

CAUTION —ET-HAND

ART. 106 - It shall be lawful for any civil officer... to arrest offenders.

NOW, G.I. JOE DISAPPEARED AFTER SMASHING CPL. CUNNINGHAM'S MESS KIT, VALUE 27¢. THIS HAS TO BE PRORATED AMONG 212 PRIVATES, 24 PFCs, 9 CORPORALS, 7 ASSORTED SERGEANTS, 1 WARRANT OFFICER, 3 2ND LIEU-TENANTS, 2 1ST LIEUTENANTS, 1 CAPTAIN. OKAY, A CAPTAIN'S SALARY FIGURES $7\frac{1}{5}$ TIMES A BUCK PRIVATE'S. SO IF WE CALL X THE PRIVATE'S SALARY THEN 7.2X IS THE CAPTAIN'S. A 1ST LIEUTENANT'S IS 6.1X. A 2ND LIEUTENANT'S IS 5.8X. MASTER AND FIRST SERGEANT'S 3.9X. TECH SERGEANT'S 3.4X....

WHAT ABOUT CLASS A ALLOTMENTS?

ART. 105 - Where the offender can not be ascertained, but [his] organization... is known,... the amount of damages inflicted may be... assessed in... proportion... upon the individual members... with such organization...

Articles of War
Part XI

t. Dave Berger
Britain

HMMM!
I SUSPECT
FOUL PLAY...

ART. 113 - When at any post, fort, camp, any person... found dead under circumstances which appear to require investigation...

AND NOW, WHAT AM I BID FOR THIS PFC RATING...

RT. 112 - ... [a] summary court shall . convert into cash by public ... sale . all effects of deceased [soldier]...

ART. 111 - Every person tried by general court martial shall, on demand... be entitled to a copy of the record of the trial

ART. 115 ... the president of a court-martial ... may appoint an interpreter, who shall interpret for the court...

ART. 110 - Articles 1, 2, and 29, 54 to 96, inclusive, and 104 to 109, inclusive, ... shall be read and explained once every six months to the soldiers... in the service

Articles of War
Part XII

Dave Breger
Britain

ART. 118 - No officer shall be discharged ...from the service except by order of the President...

ART. 116 - An assistant trial judge advocate... shall be competent to perform any duty devolved ...upon the trial judge advocate of the court

ART. 119- ...when two or more officers of the same grade are... in the same field the President may assign the command...

ART. 120- When different corps... duty together, the officer highest rank... shall command the whole

ART. 121- Any officer or soldier who believes himself wronged by his commanding officer... may complain to the commanding general...

Package from Home

Latrine

IT MAKES THE MARRIED MEN FEEL MORE AT HOME!

General Orders
Part I

Lt. Dave Breger
Britain

No. 1 — To take charge of this p[ost]
and all Government property [in]
view.

No. 2 — To walk my post in a military manner, keeping always on the alert and observing everything that takes place within sight or hearing.

No.3- To report all violations of orders I am instructed to enforce.

No. 4- To repeat all calls from posts more distant from the guard-house than my own.

No. 5- To quit my post only when properly relieved.

General Orders
Part II

Lt. Dave Breger
Britain

No 6 - To receive, obey, and pass on to the sentinel who relieves me all orders from the commanding officer, officer of the day, and officers and noncommissioned officers of the guard only.

No. 7 - To talk to no one except in the line of duty.

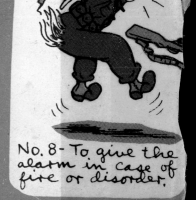

No. 8 - To give the alarm in case of fire or disorder.

No 9. To call the corporal of the guard in any case not covered by instructions.

No. 10- To salute all officers and all colors and standards not cased.

No 11- To be especially watchful at night and, during the time for challenging, to challenge all persons on or near my post, and to allow no one to pass without proper authority

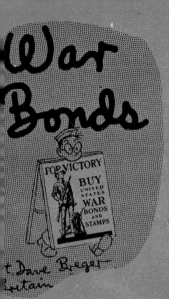

X-Ray

Dentist

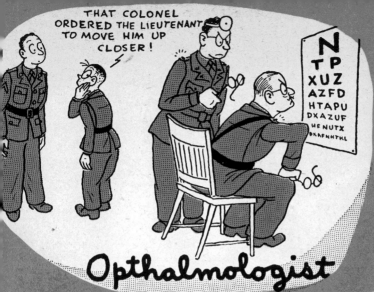

Opthalmologist

Sick Call

Inoculation

U.S.O.
Camp
Shows

Dave Breger
Britain

G. I. talent

Variety

Chairborne Troops

Lt. Dave Breger
Britain.

New Year
1944

I hereby resolve...

t. Dave Breger
Britain

to pass inspections

to make no complaints about
the food

-that enlisted mens' bil-
lets have privacy and
comforts of home

that officers show due
respect on meeting en-
listed men in public

-but I suppose I'd realize there's a
war to win, so everything would
be the same as before.

Fire-Watch
Part III

Action

Transport

Fire power

General Hospital

Lt. Dave Breger
Britain

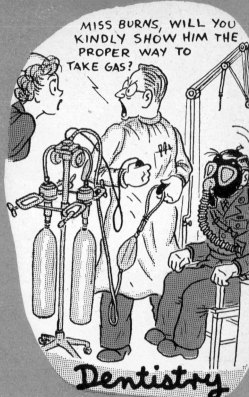

Dentistry

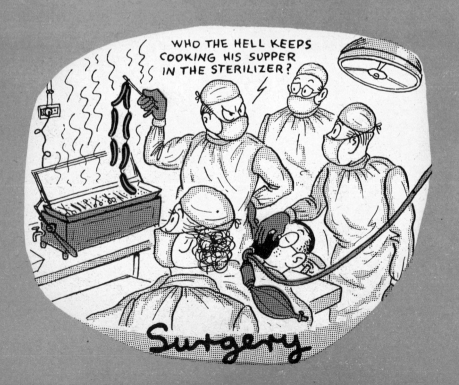

Surgery

Army Nurse

Special Service

t. Dave Breger
Britain

Morale

Publications

Engineers

OME OF US ARE WHISKEY MEN AND SOME OF US DRINK GIN,
DON'T KNOW WHERE WE'RE GOING BUT WE LIKE IT WHERE WE'VE BEEN,
OME OF US DRINK SPANISH RUM AND SOME DRINK BEER AND ALE,
EVERY TIME WE SEE A JUG WE SET IT ON IT'S TAIL .
NOT SO MUCH THE ORNAMENTS THAT MAKE US WHAT WE ARE ,
LL COULD WEAR CROSSED GUNS OR WINGS AND MOST COULD WEAR A STAR,
THE WAY WE STAND AND THE WAY WE SPIT AND THE WAY WE CUT THE AIR ,
S REALLY THE MEN WHO ARE UNDERNEATH THE UNIFORM WE WEAR .

AY DOWN ALL THEIR ROLLING ROADS AND CUT DOWN ALL THEIR TREES,
IF THE ORDERS EVER CAME WE'D FORGE THE RAGING SEAS.
NEVER THEY WANT TO SLEEP AWHILE WE PUT THEM UP A TOWN,
WE BUILD THE BLASTED BRIDGES SO THE INFANTRY WON'T DROWN.
ET THEM OVER RIVERS AND ACROSS THE MOUNTAIN STREAMS .
VERYTHING BUT TUCK THEM IN AND WISH THEM PLEASANT DREAMS.
WHEN THE GOING'S REALLY TOUGH AND SHELLS BURST IN THEIR EARS,
HOLE DIVISION'S APT TO PRAY, "GOD, SEND FOUR ENGINEERS !"

RUMORED ABOUT THE NAVY, WHICH HAS A LOVE FOR SPORT,
EVERY SINGLE SAILOR HAS A GIRL IN EVERY PORT.
EVERY COMBAT ENGINEER, WHO DOESN'T NEED TO BOAST,
A WIFE IN EVERY VILLAGE THAT ISN'T ON THE COAST.
WOMEN FAINT BY DOZENS WHEN THEY SEE US MARCHING BY,
ICK THEM UP AND DUST THEM OFF AND SET THEM OUT TO DRY.
E GOT A LINE THE SIGNAL CORPS AND CAVALRY CAN'T BEAT,
YOU CAN'T TALK LOVE AND RADIO, AND HORSES DON'T SMELL SWEET.

AN TRACE OUR FIGHTING HISTORY THROUGH A HUNDRED THOUSAND YEARS,
WHEN THEY NEEDED BARRICADES THEY SENT FOR ENGINEERS.
AS A VERY HAIRY EARLY SOLDIER OF THE CORPS
DISCOVERED BOWS AND ARROWS AND LEARNED WHAT ROCKS WERE FOR
BUILT THE HORSE THAT GOT TROY GIGGED WHEN HOMER WAS A PUP
WE RAN AHEAD AT MARATHON AND TRIPPED THE PERSIANS UP.
N CAESAR CROSSED THE RUBICON AS HE WAS GOING HOME,
UT A BRIDGE ACROSS THE STREAM AND CHANGED THE COURSE OF ROME.

LEON AT WATERLOO MIGHT STILL HAVE HELD THE FIELD
HAD HAD TEN ENGINEERS TO KEEP OLD BLÜCHER HEELED.
WELLINGTON, HAD WE BEEN THERE INSTEAD OF HIS ARRAY,
D HAVE TAKEN HALF AN HOUR TO WIN INSTEAD OF HALF A DAY.
ME OF US ARE BOURBON MEN AND SOME OF US DRINK WINE,
THERE'S MORE MEAT IN FRONT OF US WHEN WE SIT DOWN TO DINE.
EN THE AVERAGE CANNONEER GOES DOWN TO HELL IN TEARS,
FIND THE STYX AND PHLEGATHON WERE BRIDGED BY ENGINEERS.

S/SGT. HARRY BROWN

Dave Breger
Britain

WATCH OUT! THE ENEMY HAS TONS OF POPCORN STORED AS FLAME DEFENSE!

Assault

WE'RE BADLY IN NEED OF MORE EQUIPMENT.... SOLDIER, GO OUT AND SELL A LOT OF WAR BONDS!

Air Fields

Making Money

Dave Breger
Britain

See a real live AMERICAN **INDIAN** FROM CHICAGO!
(Open to British Public only)
ADMISSION
CIVILIANS......3 SHILLINGS
H.M. FORCES....3 SHILLINGS
GIRLS (AGES 16-28) FREE

U.S.

U.S. ARMY COMPLAINT DEPT.
GRIPES FIXED UP
@ 5 SHILLINGS PER GRIPE

No promotions?   Food lousey?
Ordered around?   Billets rotten?
Reveille too early?   Sergeants mean?
Rank pulled on you?   Inspections?
No furloughs?   No transfer?
"WE FIX *ANY* GRIPE"

THE PROVO.ST-MARSHAL WOULD LIKE TO SEE YOU!

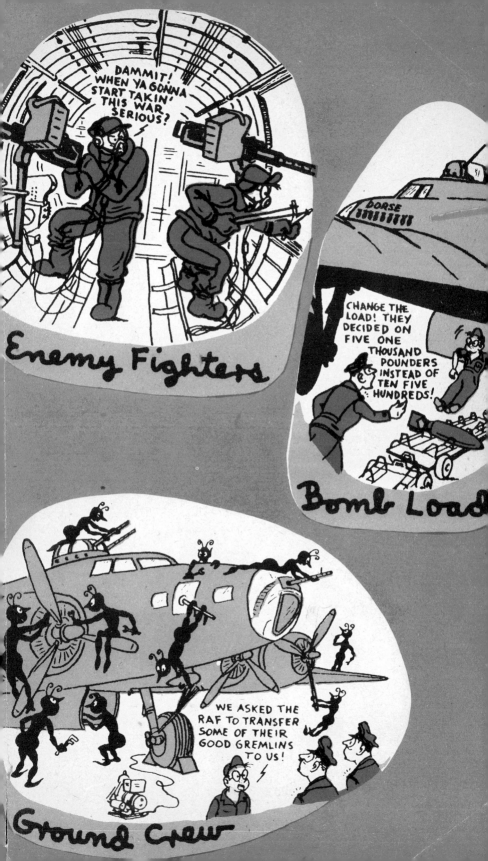